Dilemma

David Walker

Edward Arnold   N.O.H.S.

© David Walker 1979
First published 1979 by
Edward Arnold (Publishers) Ltd
41 Bedford Square, London WC1B 3DQ

Reprinted 1979, 1980, 1982, 1983

British Library Cataloguing in Publication Data
Walker, David, b. 1947
Dilemmas.
I. Title
822'.9'14   PR 6073.A39/

ISBN 0-7131-0320-5

Set in 11/12pt IBM Journal by 𝓐 Tek Art, Croydon, Surrey.
Printed and bound in Great Britain by Spottiswoode Ballantyne Limited, Colchester and London.

Preface

These plays, intended to cut across subject boundaries and be dealt with in English, Drama, Social Studies and Liberal Education classes, present problem situations which have to be resolved through talk, writing and improvisation. They look at questions which don't necessarily have easy answers, and are followed by comprehensive and carefully structured suggestions. These lead from simple evaluative remarks about the script into much larger demands which require the readers to think outside their own situation and suggest remedies for some of the social and moral questions they will probably have to face, or are facing already.

The plays concentrate on the moral dilemmas and value judgements that have to be faced, rather than the hard-core topics which are more readily identifiable social problems.

Contents

Alfabet

Mark	(Twin brothers)	Mother	
Trevor		'Alfabet'	(A tramp)
Alison	(Sisters)	Sean	(Two friends)
Mary		Greg	

Mark and Trevor are walking their dog over some waste ground near their home.

Mark   I know what I'm going to do when I leave school.

Trevor picks up a stick and throws it for the dog. . .

Trevor   What?

Mark   Army. I'm joining up.

Trevor   You're mad, you wouldn't catch me in there. . . . too much being told what to do and when to breathe.

Mark   It's a good life. Adventure, fresh air . . .

Trevor   You get mothered I suppose. . . . get your washing done and your bed made.

Mark   (*angry*) Leave off.

Trevor   Well! You swap your freedom for a bit of organisation.

Mark   You know where you stand; there's no crime in that.

Trevor   (*distracted*) What's that dog doing? It gets dafter by the day . . . can't even bring a stick back now.

Mark   He looks like he's found something.

Trevor   He behaves like a mongrel.

Mark   He is a mongrel.

Trevor   He never is . . . he's a pedigree!

The dog begins to bark and snap at its discovery.

Trevor   Come on, we'd better get down there before the neighbours call the dog catcher . . . you know what they're like round here.

Mark   La-di-da lot.

Tevor   Come on then.

They run after the dog.

Back at home, **Alison** *and* **Mary** *are with* **Mum.** *They are washing up.*

Alison   Mum, Mary won't dry.
Mary   Who said?
Alison   She won't mum . . . look at this pile. How am I supposed to wash up if she won't dry?
Mother   Stop it you two. You're always the same these days. When are you ever going to stop arguing?
Mary   She keeps flicking water at me mum.
Mum   Come on now.
Mary   I hate housework. I'd rather do anything than housework.
Mum   You'll have to get used to it sooner or later young lady. It's something everybody has to do. Especially women. In fact only women most of the time!
Mary   I don't see the point.
Alison   Make her do the dusting then mum if she can't do this properly. . . .
Mary   (*shouting*) Shut up Alison!
Mum   Now then Mary.
Mary   (*exasperated*) Oh . . . I'm going out. . . .

She flings the drying towel on the floor and runs out of the house.

At the waste ground, **Mark** *and* **Trevor** *have reached the dog.*

Trevor   Come on dog, stop your yacking.
Mark   It's a load of cardboard boxes.
Trevor   Yeah . . . they're big ones.

He kicks one and a shaky voice shouts from inside. . .

Voice   Stop it. Get off and leave me alone. Go on, get away.

Mark *and* **Trevor** *jump back startled.*

Trevor   Who's in there? Who is it? Come on . . . we'll set the dog on you.

An old **Tramp** *emerges looking very tatty.*

Tramp   Leave me alone. Clear off. I don't want you.
Trevor   What are you doing here?
Tramp   Clear off.

Trevor   You can't stay here. This is private property.
Tramp   I'm not going anywhere. I'm staying here. I bet you
I am . . . I'm staying.
Trevor   (*a little bewildered*) You can't bet me.
Tramp   I bet you're going to get me something to eat.
Trevor   I bet you I'm not!
Mark   I will.
Tramp   I knew you would. I bet you can't be back before I
count to three. One two three. . . .
Trevor   Where have you come from? What's your name?
Tramp   Why what's yours?
Trevor   What is it?
Tramp   I bet you can't guess.
Trevor   No.
Tramp   Alf. . . .
Trevor   Alf what?
Tramp   (*laughing*) 'Alfabet'. Always a bet with 'Alfabet'. . . .
Trevor   You're a nutter. I'll have to bring a few of my mates
down here and get rid of you.
Mark   Leave off Trev. He isn't doing any harm.
Trevor   He's spoiling the neighbourhood. Look at him. Dirty
old fella.

Mary *arrives.*

Mary   Hey you two. . . what are you doing?
Mark   Come here.
Mary   What's up?
Mark   Look.
Trevor   A tramp!
Mary   Poor fella. He looks hungry. (*To the* **Tramp**) Do you
want some food?
Tramp   Hello girl. Yes I do. Food.
Trevor   I'm going to see the lads. . . (*He leaves*)
Mary   What a shame. (*To* **Mark**) What can we do?
Mark   (*to the* **Tramp**) Where do you live?
Tramp   I bet you can't guess. Go on. I bet you. . . .
Mark   (*to* **Mary**) He's like that all the time . . . betting.
Mary   Let's go home and get him some food.
Mark   All right I'll stand here while you get some.
Mary   OK.

She leaves. . . .
There is a long silence. **Mark** *eventually speaks.*

7

Mark   Why are you a tramp mister?

Tramp   Nowhere to live.

Mark   You could have joined the Army. It's a good life. Adventure, fresh air.

Tramp   Mind your own business. (*He takes out a bottle and drinks*)

Mark   What's that?

Tramp   Mind your own business. (*He puts the top on the bottle and suddenly gets up*) . . . I'm going.

Mark   Hang on a minute. My sister's gone to get some food.

Tramp   I bet you she hasn't. Give us 20p for a cup of tea.

Mark   I haven't got any money.

Tramp   I bet you have little lad . . . come on give us 10p.

Meanwhile **Trevor** *has rounded up a few of his mates and is approaching from the other direction.*

Trevor   He's down on the waste ground . . . behind our house. Dirty old fella he is.

Greg   Are we going to move him on then?

Trevor   Something like that.

Sean   Bit of a warning eh? Nuisance these tramps. Don't think we should allow it myself.

Trevor   Now's your chance to do your bit. There's a lot of people sitting around talking, letting these tramps and what have you take over.

Greg   They'll be telling us what to do next.

Sean   Dead right.

Trevor   Let's get down there.

Mary *returns to the spot where she left* **Mark** *and the* **Tramp** *to find they are gone.*

Mary   Mark. Mark, where are you? I've got the food Mark. (*To herself*) Where can they be? I wonder what's happened? . . . Mark where are you? Mark!

Alison *has followed her without being noticed.*

Alison   So, here you are. I thought I saw you sneak out of the kitchen with that food. Who's it for? Come on, tell me what's going on . . . .

Starting points
1 How do you think the tramp came to be called 'Alfabet'?
2 Trevor disapproves of having life organised for him — why then does he also disapprove of 'Alfabet'? How is this attitude different to Mark's?
3 Why do you think the sisters are in doors working when the brothers are roaming the neighbourhood?
4 What do you think Alison's attitude to the tramp would be?

Discussion points
5 How does it come about that we have, and refer to people, as tramps? What problems do they face and how can we help them?
6 Whose way of solving problems is best — Trevor's or Mary's?

Written work
7 Write a conversation between the tramp and Mark, showing how his lack of normal contact with people confuses Mark.
8 Write a scene where local residents are meeting together to unite against some sort of threat which they feel will injure their quality of life. It might be that there are plans to build a hostel for 'down and outs' or a re-housing programme of some sort. What sort of stands will be made and what sort of attitudes exposed?

Action
9 Imagine 'Alfabet' goes to a Salvation Army hostel. Work out a scene to improvise showing a group of similar people meeting and talking. It could be late evening when each one is reflecting on the past.
10 Collect as many news items or articles as possible to illustrate the problems of homelessness and share the information amongst the class. Work out your own remedies and see how your own community is dealing with the problem. This might mean a visit or a letter to the relevant organisations. Be fair and honest in your conclusions though — don't blame or accuse until you have the facts.

Me, A Father?

Mum   John
Dad   Bernard
Heather   (their daughter)   Nurse
James   (Heather's husband)

Heather *is being visited by her parents after giving birth to a baby girl.*

Mother   (*looking at the baby*) Congratulations love. She's beautiful.

Dad   Just like her grandad she is.

Heather   (*playfully*) Never! She's like James. Look at her mouth. . . .

Mother   I shouldn't worry who she's like my love. She's all in one piece and that's the most important thing. Look at her sleeping; aren't they lovely when they're like that?

Dad   They're only fooling. You wait a few more days and you'll know she's about.

Mother   She's beautiful.

Heather   She's always sleeping: she even falls asleep when she's feeding; I have to keep pinching her toes.

Mother   Can we take her out of the cot for a few minutes?

Heather   Not really mum. They don't like us mauling them about during visiting time.

Mother   It's not mauling about. My goodness, I've handled more babies than half of these young nurses put together.

Dad   You're feeling broody mother. I know it. There'll be plenty of time for you to nurse the youngster when she comes home.

Heather   Thanks dad.

Mum   I never saw your father around much when there were nappies to be changed. 'Course I suppose it's all disposable nowadays isn't it?

10

Heather Yes, in here. But it won't be when I get out. They're too expensive.

Mother It's different now . . . easier . . . not like it used to be.

Heather Maybe.

Dad Stop moaning woman. We're here to share the girl's happiness.

Mum Oh I'm sorry love. (*Reaching into her bag*) Here, I've brought you some magazines.

Heather Oh thanks mum. That's smashing.

Mother And some toothpaste you asked for.

Heather Lovely.

Pause.

Mother Has James been down?

Heather Not yet . . . he's coming though.

Mother Good.

Dad He's made a lovely job of the baby's room.

Heather Has he?

Dad I should say so. Fit for a King.

Heather Queen.

Dad King or Queen. Light yellow — it's smashing.

The **Nurse** *arrives. . .*

Nurse Time to go now please. Sorry to push you away but baby must have some rest. (*She walks on*)

Dad Rest! The baby's done nothing but rest all the time we've been here.

Mother Come on then father. Now is there anything else you want Heather?

Heather I don't think so.

James *arrives. . . .*

James Is it time to go?

Heather (*delighted to see him*) James! Hello love. It's lovely to see you. Come and see the baby.

Mother We'll leave you two together.

Dad Yes. See you tomorrow.

They leave.

Heather Look, isn't she lovely?

James (*half-hearted*) Yes.

Heather Don't you think so?

11

James   'Course I do. I said I did and I do.

Heather   What's the matter?

James   There's nothing the matter.

Heather   (*trying to change the subject*) Dad says what a good job you made of her room.

James   Oh.

Heather   Would you like a chocolate?

James   No.

The Nurse *returns.*

Nurse   Come along now. You're over time as it is. The other patients want to get changed and start their feeding.

James   I'm going.

Heather   Sorry.

She goes. . .

Heather   Try and come sooner tomorrow.

James   I'll try. It's not easy though, I'm working late.

Heather   Working late?

James   Yes . . . working late. You'll have to get used to that now there's another mouth to feed. We can't just do what we want any more.

Heather   It's not as bad as that.

James   I'll have to go. I'll see you.

He walks away.

Heather   Bye love. . . .

Later that evening James *is in a pub with his mates.*

John   How goes it mate?

James   Not bad.

John   I'd say I'd seen you looking better. What's getting you down?

James   I'm all right.

Bernard   Post natal depression John, that's what it is.

James   Shut up you two. I'm all right I told you. I don't see why you have to go round picking holes in people if they aren't laughing all over their faces.

John   Only trying to help . . . keep calm now. Helping an old mate out of the doldrums.

James   Sorry.

Bernard   I was serious anyway. You can't expect to become a

father without it changing your whole life.
James Me, a father?
Bernard That's what you are my friend. Never thought it would happen did you? Nor me when I had mine. It takes some getting used to. I understand.
John I'm glad I'm out of it then if that's what it does to you. Makes me wonder why anybody ever gets married and has a family if this is the outcome.
Bernard It doesn't last long.
James I don't feel anything for it. It just lies there. Heather's making me say it's lovely when it's not . . . it's no more than a doll to me.
Bernard A real doll . . . and that's the difference.
John I think I'll go for something to eat. Anybody coming?
Bernard Not tonight squire.
John James?
James Can't afford it.
John Ah well. It looks as if I'm dining alone. See you.

He leaves.

Bernard Don't worry James. It'll all come out right in the end.
James I hope so.
Bernard When is she due home?
James Next Wednesday.
Bernard Wednesday . . . (*reflecting*) . . . not bad, it's a decent TV night Wednesday.

Later in the week — Wednesday evening.
Heather *is home but the baby has been kept in hospital because of jaundice.*

Heather (*entering the house*) It's great to be back.
James I'll make you some tea in a minute.
Heather No. That's all right. I can manage.
James Seems funny that you've come home without the baby. Like it never happened.
Heather I must admit I feel funny being away from it. It's been part of me for so long now. Still, nothing to worry about. She'll be better in a few days.
James How are you?
Heather Fine. Dad said how you'd made the bedroom look nice . . . I'm dying to see it.
James Not yet. . .

Heather   I can't wait James!

James   Later.

Heather   All right. (*Brighter*) How are you?

James   OK.

Heather   What's it like being a dad?

James   I don't feel any different.

Heather   Wait till she's with us all the time and running round shouting 'daddy'!

James   How old are you Heather?

Heather   Why?

James   Go on, how old?

Heather   You know how old I am. I'm 19.

James   So am I.

Heather   And. . . . ?

James   I sometimes wonder . . . I sometimes wonder what we've got ourselves into . . .

Heather   (*upset*) James! We talked about it. We know why we did it. We want our own family.

James   Maybe.

Heather   It's just as hard for me you know.

James   That's just what I'm saying. So what's the point?

Heather   There doesn't have to be any point; people have babies.

James   We are now parents.

Heather   I know, but that doesn't make us monsters or anything. We haven't changed . . . we're only doing what everybody else does.

James   You'd better come with me and see the bedroom.

Heather   (*surprised*) Not now James.

James   I thought you wanted to . . . you said you couldn't wait a minute ago.

Heather   (*upset by him*) James!

James   (*taking her by the hand*) Come on.

He stamps upstairs with her and throws the bedroom door open . . .

Heather   (*startled*) James! What have you done?

James   I threw it, everywhere . . .

Heather   Why?

James   I painted it so that it looked like a work of art and then I picked up the orange paint and threw it — everywhere. . . . What do you think of that?

14

Starting points
1 What do *you* think of that? Why has James done it? Is he being completely selfish?
2 Are either of James' friends any help to him?
3 Do you think it makes things worse/more difficult because the baby has had to remain in hospital?
4 Heather has been understanding so far — can she be for much longer? Can she look to her parents for support?

Discussion points
5 How much understanding do you think is needed in a marriage and when does genuine give and take become bullying by one partner or another?
6 Who do you think has responsibility for holding a situation like this together? Is there anyone to turn to apart from family and friends? What part can family and friends play in helping a marriage?

Written work
7 Write, in the form of a play or essay, what you think happens during the rest of the day.
8 The only person not considered so far is the baby. Imagine that by some miracle she can talk to other babies for a few minutes. Imagine they are together in a nursery and write some of the conversation they have as they discuss their own parents and situations together.

Action
9 Imagine Heather and James are invited to appear on a television programme which is discussing the difficulties of parenthood. Work out a scene to show them discussing the problem along with others like them and social workers, educationalists, psychologists and a family doctor. You could try to create a studio atmosphere by arranging camera positions, interviews, technicians and other production detail.
10 Will you marry and have children?
Find as much information as you can about other ways of bringing up children. See how other countries and communities do it — especially the primitive ones. Document your findings and compare the reasons for the respective

15

methods and choose one which appears most successful to you. Next, concentrate on our society and interview some parents and find out what they think the ideal family situation is and how they have coped with having children. You should be in a better position now to answer the question . . . 'will you'?

Red Flag

Bob
Roger
Mary   (four friends)
Annette
Beach Attendant

Lifeguard
Man
Woman
1st Child   (7 years old)
2nd Child   (5 years old)

Bob, Roger, Mary *and* Annette *are leaving the station after a long train journey. They are heading for the beach.*

Mary   Thank goodness we're off the train. I was beginning to wish we'd never started.

Annette   Me too. I hate the smell of trains — I always have done; it's a sickly stale smell.

Bob   Come on, I'm bursting to get down to the beach and see what the surf's like.

Mary   I just hope there is some, otherwise you'll be disappointed.

Roger   There's always some, even if it's only a swell, and that might be best for our first try.

Bob   If it's as exciting as I think it's going to be we'll book a holiday down here. What do you think? We could hire a chalet or caravan or something.

Annette   Good idea. I love it here. I could be a beachcomber and have no regrets.

Roger   The last time I was here I sat and watched them surfing for days. I always wanted to have a go.

Mary   I love the seaside.

Annette   Where do we get surf boards from?

Bob   Down on the beach, don't we Roger?

Roger   Yes. It's big business down there. You'll see the beach full of surfers. They're surfing mad here. Cars drive about with boards on top, people carry them, sunbathe on them, polish them, talk about them. It's an experience.

Mary   How long have we?

Annette   What's the time now? (*Looking at her watch*) Twelve, and the train leaves at 5 o'clock. Five hours.

Bob   Let's get a move on then. The beach isn't far.

Roger   There's a path down from the cliffs which is quicker . . . follow me.

The four people reach the cliff. They are breathless and fighting against the wind. They reach the edge and look down at the sea.

Bob   Look at that!

Roger   What a sight.

Mary   The wind's blowing me over.

Annette   It's worth every minute of that horrible train ride. I love it. Look at the colours. Blue and white and brown.

Roger   It looks great from up here. I wonder what it's like down there?

Bob   The sea looks gigantic.

Roger   It does.

Mary   Why is it empty?

Annette   It's beautiful — empty.

Roger   I wonder?

Mary   There's nobody at all in the water.

Roger   Let's go and see.

They climb down the cliff.
At the bottom . . .

Roger   It's worse than ever down here. We'll never surf in this.

Annette   What!

Bob   The red flags are flying.

Roger   Where?

Bob   Both ends of the beach.

Roger   Oh yeah.

Mary   Can't we just go in the edge? It's a long way to come for nothing.

Annette   Do you think it'll stop before we go?

Roger   Can't tell. . . .

Bob   There's a board hire over there.

They move over to talk to the attendant.

Attendant   Hello there.

Roger   Any chance?

Attendant   Doubtful. When it comes in westerly like this it could be blowing for days. Dangerous too. You gets all sorts

18

of funny currents round the rocks. Drag you down like litter.

Annette We've come miles as well.

Attendant Not worth it is it?

Mary Can we hire boards?

Attendant No point.

Mary I thought we could just mess about in the edge.

Attendant It's the drag, the undertow. These waves could suck you down, back along and into the surf.

Bob Damn!

The Lifeguard *arrives.* ...

Lifeguard No surfing to-day kids.

Bob No?

Lifeguard No surfing, no bathing. The flags are out.

Annette What a disappointment.

Mary Are there any beaches more sheltered than this?

Lifeguard No. When it comes in like this the whole of this coast is out of action.

Bob You're sure we couldn't just go in the edge?

Attendant (*To* Lifeguard) People never believe us.

Lifeguard (*To* Roger) You'd be surprised how many characters ignore warnings. They think the sea's a bubble bath — there to be played with and swished around their toes. It's a killer. A monster when it's like this . . . stay out of it.

Roger OK we will. It's just that we were looking forward to it and we've come a long way.

Mary Let's go into those dunes over there and have some of our sandwiches.

Annette Why not.

Roger (*To* Lifeguard) Thanks.

They begin to walk away. ...

Attendant Sorry.

Bob We would have given a lot for a go — just five minutes.

Attendant It's not worth the risk.

They trudge along the beach feeling very disappointed. They settle eventually into a hollow which is sheltered from the wind.

Roger I could spit.

Annette I still think it'd be worth a holiday.

Mary Me too.

Bob Let's come then, in the summer.

They hear voices coming across the dunes. A **Man**, *his wife and two young children are approaching. They are struggling with a newly purchased inflatable boat.*

Man Come on soldiers. Press on, we'll soon be there. Fall in mother. We've got the beach to ourselves by the look of things. Peace and quiet — launching the boat into the 'briny'. Step on it there, we haven't got all day.

1st Child I'm tired.

Man Nonsense.

2nd Child I don't want to swim. It's too cold.

Man Character building stuff all this. Here we are — what about this for a spot?

The family walk by unnoticed.

Man Don't let the boat drag mother. The sharp stones will shred her in no time.

Woman It's very heavy.

Man We're here now. (*Stopping to look at the beach*) Look at that! What a sight. Pure joy. Bristling with pleasure. . . just offering a challenge!

Woman It's ever so windy. I don't think we ought to go in the water.

1st Child I want to swim.

2nd Child I want to go in my boat.

1st Child It's not your boat. It's all our boat.

2nd Child Dad says it's mine.

Man Silence in the ranks, thank you. The craft is to share between us all. We'll launch her shortly. Right. (*They put everything down*) Now for it. . . .

1st Child Can I have a drink of water?

Woman Ask your father dear.

1st Child Can I have a drink dad?

Man Certainly not young man. Into your swimming costumes everybody.

2nd Child It's too cold.

Man Nonsense.

He changes and the rest follow suit.

Woman Do you think we should swim dear?

Man Certainly, why not?

20

Woman Nobody else is swimming.

Man I wouldn't be where I am now if I'd done what everybody else did all my life.

Woman The red flags are flying.

Man (*scoffing*) Red flags! We're going soft in this country. They put those things out when there's a ripple on the surface. . . .

Silence as everyone changes. . . .

Right then. One at each corner. . . .

They lift the boat. . . .

1st Child We can't all get in here dad.

Man Certainly we can. Improvisation my boy. All ready? Forward then.

The young people watch them down the beach into the water.

Mary What a performance!

Annette What a man! How do people live with people like that?

Bob They're mad.

Roger Do you think we should warn the lifeguard?

They watch in silence as the family launch the flimsy craft and climb in. They are soon awash and the man scrambles the two children out as a wave crashes down on them. He takes them ashore and turns to see the woman clinging to the upturned boat as it is sucked into the heavy surf.

Roger Can you see what's happening down there?

Bob Too well.

Roger Poor woman!

Mary What can we do?

Annette We can get the lifeguard for a start. (*She runs off to tell him*)

Bob There isn't going to be time.

Roger Do we go in after her?

Mary I could see it happening.

Roger We can't just sit here.

*The **Man** looks about him and sees the group in the dunes. . . . He starts shouting towards them asking for help.*

Mary He's seen us now.
Bob It should be him clinging to that boat. . . .
Roger But it isn't is it — so what are we going to do?

Starting points
1 Did the family deserve what it got? Should the four friends have to be involved?
2 Do you think they should go into the water to help?
3 What do you think of the attitude of the man? How does this attitude affect people around him?
4 What do you think the lifeguard's reaction will be when he arrives on the scene?

Discussion points
5 What would you do? Can you ignore people who are in trouble in this way? Would you be in a position to help in the first aid process if you did give assistance? Do you think we should all know some first aid?
6 Where else do people ignore warnings of danger? Whose responsibility is it to decide when a situation is a dangerous one? How much of the element of danger should people be allowed to introduce into their lives?

Written work
7 Describe the situation from the point of view of the woman. . . .
or
Write an account of the accident as recorded by the man to some of his acquaintances at a later date.
8 Imagine a local pressure group wants to have the beach closed to the public because they feel it is too dangerous and accidents keep happening despite the warnings. An independent body asks the lifeguard for a written report of his views and experiences over the past weeks.

Action
9 Improvise a scene where someone in authority, like a policeman, a steward or a marshal tries to tell an awkward person that something he or she is attempting is dangerous. Involve bystanders.
10 It has been said, 'No man is an island'. Discuss what you think this means and how true you think it is. Devise a

short questionnaire and interview a range of people to discover how much or how little they think we should be involved in the lives of others. Try to find if there is a point at which people refuse to be involved — in this case it might be when one's own safety is involved. Present your conclusions in the clearest way you think fit and write an appropriate sentence to sum up your findings.

Stale Mate

Father
Mother
Ian   (their son)
Pamela   (their daughter)
Sally
Gary

Mandy
John
Valerie
Mr Eliot
Secretary

It is tea time as **Ian** *and his* **Mother** *and* **Father** *settle down to eat.* **Ian** *is scouring through the situations vacant column.*

Father   No luck today then, son?

Ian   No.

Father   Where did you go?

Ian   Job Centre; but it's the same old story. They haven't had any jobs in for ages. I'm just looking through here in case there's anything new. I think I've seen them all before. . . . but you never know.

Mother   I don't know what the world's coming to I'm sure. I thought unemployment was a thing of the past.

Father   So did we all.

Mother   It's eight months now.

Ian   It doesn't half get you down.

Mother   I only hope things get better.

Father   After all that schooling and qualifications.

Ian   Anything just to be working.

Mother   What about going to College or something, Ian?

Ian   I might have to.

Father   What about working in the goods office at my place?

Ian   What?

Father   There's a job going . . . but I don't like to suggest it because it's nothing like you wanted . . . and I don't want you to feel as though I'm pushing.

Ian   I'd jump at it dad. What is it?

24

Father Paper work, checking addresses and despatches and what have you.

Mother Would you like to Ian?

Ian I would yeah . . . I really would.

Father It's decent wages I know because Alan Stewart has it now.

Mother Why is he leaving?

Father Emigrating.

Ian Great dad. What do I have to do?

Father They haven't advertised it yet I know — so if you went up there tomorrow and sort of presented yourself about half-past ten you might do yourself some good.

Ian At last!

Mother (*to* **Father**) Have you arranged all this?

Father In a way, but there's no guarantee he'll get it — they just said the manager would have a chat with him round about ten thirty.

Mother Oh — thank goodness for that.

Father It would be a start wouldn't it?

Ian And money.

Mother That's the best news we've had for weeks.

Ian Wait till I tell Sally.

The Foyer of a local cinema later in the evening.
Ian, Sally, Gary, Mandy, John *and* **Valerie** *are waiting to go in.*

John Where would we be without the pictures? Nowhere warm and dark to go!

Valerie John!

John Fancy a hot dog?

Valerie No thank you — I've just had my tea.

Ian It's the best tea time we've had for ages.

John Oh yeah?

Ian Chance of a job at last.

Gary Where's that?

Ian My dad's place, in the stores. Nothing much, but it's work, and after all this time out of work I'll take anything.

Gary Lucky you.

Ian Still nothing for you?

Gary No.

Mandy You wouldn't want a stores job, though, would you Gary? I mean you've got qualifications.

Gary Anything . . . same as Ian. I'm not choosy any more.

Mandy   I thought you were going to be a manager. You told me you were. You'll never have any money if you work in stores.

Sally   It's no disgrace to take a job like that.

Ian   Work's work and I've grown up a bit recently. There's no reason to think there's only one sort of job good enough. People are people and jobs are jobs.

Gary   Right. Tell us more Ian.

Ian   I'm going up there tomorrow. They haven't advertised yet but my dad reckons they'll be happy to listen if I get there and ask for an interview. Can't hurt can it? It's almost certain anyway . . . my dad's had a word with the personnel manager.

Gary   What time's your interview?

Ian   Half-past ten . . . about.

Mandy   Can I have some chocolate Gary?

Gary   No. I haven't any money.

Mandy   (*disgusted. Taking money out of her pocket*) Men are supposed to pay for women you know. It's part of a man's job to escort his woman and offer refreshments and things.

John   Are we ready to go in yet?

Sally   Has the other film finished?

John   Finishing now — come on.

Ian   Right then, let's go.

They enter. . . .
The following morning.
Ian *is getting ready to go for the interview.*

Mother   (*finishing ironing his shirt*) I'll just air this for a few minutes before you put it on.

Ian   Thanks mum. (*Polishing his shoes*) I haven't seen my shoes like this for ages.

Mother   Impressions are important. I don't care what people say, they take notice of your appearance. It counts for a lot.

Ian   It's good of dad to sort it out like this for me.

Mother   He was worried you might think he was interfering. He said last night he couldn't decide whether to say anything or not. He's encouraged you all these years to try hard at school and when you leave and can't get work — well he feels as though he's let you down.

Pamela *enters.*

Pamela   Mum I can't find my English book.

Mother It's up in your room if it's anywhere.

Pamela I can't find it. Oh well I'll just have to be late.

Mother (*angry*) You will not young lady. You'll find that book and you'll get a move on. You'll never get anywhere in life with that attitude.

She leaves and slams the door.

Ian Was I like that when I was fourteen?

Mother Probably.

Ian (*standing*) Right, time I was going.

Mum You'll be early.

Ian I'd rather be early. I'll walk and give myself time to think.

Mother Up to you. Here's your shirt, it's all right now.

Ian Thanks. I just hope I'll be opening a wage packet at the end of the week.

Later in the morning, walking towards the factory office. He climbs the steps and knocks at the enquiry hatch.

Secretary Good morning.

Ian Hello, my name's Ian Hepworth and I've come about the stores job; I know it's not been advertised yet but I wondered if I could have a word with the personnel manager?

No reply . . .

My dad works here and he sort of checked it was all right . . .

Secretary still looks puzzled. . .

I know I'm a bit early, my dad said half-past ten, but I don't mind waiting.

Secretary You're Mr Hepworth?

Ian Yes.

Secretary That's funny . . . if you'd like to take a seat, Mr Eliot will see you in a moment.

She closes the hatch door muttering confusion to herself. Ian feels a little deflated and sits down. He waits for quarter of an hour. There is no one around so he gets up and looks at the pictures on the wall.
His back is turned to the door as it opens . . . He waits to be spoken to . . . .

Mr. Eliot Ah Mr. Hepworth, come this way.

27

Ian *turns and sees* Gary *leaving the office.*

Ian   Thank you . . . Hello Gary!
Gary   (*hesitatingly*) Hello.
Ian   What are you doing?
Gary   Sorry mate, I couldn't help it.
Ian   What do you mean?
Gary   I feel lousy about it — I hoped I wouldn't see you but he kept me longer than I thought.
Ian   You mean . . . . ?
Gary   Well, you know how it is.
Ian   You're after the job!
Gary   What else?

Starting points
1 Why are Ian's mum and dad hesitant about suggesting the job?
2 What sort of general feelings about work do Ian's friends express?
3 Do you think Pamela's 'couldn't care less' attitude towards school is justified? How could you persuade her to make the most of school?
4 Do you approve of Gary's actions? Why or why not?

Discussion points
5 What values concerning jobs do you think are important? Do you want the status that some jobs offer, or are you happy to do without? What does status bring with it?
6 This situation happened because too many people were chasing too few jobs. Do you think society has a responsibility to provide work for people or should people make their own work?

Written work
7 Continue writing the play as Ian enters and begins the interview. Resolve the situation by deciding who gets the job and why.
8 Imagine you are collecting information on unemployed school leavers. Write a letter to Ian's parents asking them for any criticisms and suggestions they share about the situation as it stands. Then put yourself in their shoes and write a reply.

Action

9 Improvise a scene where a number of young people have all arrived for interviews for a job and are left for a short time together in a waiting area. What will they be saying? What will their attitude be? Who will be confident? Who will be noisy? What can you learn by watching people's behaviour? You could show one or two people eventually being interviewed. Their behaviour and attitude will obviously affect the interviewer. What do you think will impress him and what will not?

10 Collect some facts and figures on unemployment in your area and try to point out the reasons why. Show on a graph how this has been increasing or decreasing in recent years and try to predict what it will be like in the future. What do you think will happen if we have more and more free time to spend? Collect some opinions from people who are leaving school soon about what they would do with lots of free time.

Girls,Girls,Girls

Miss X	Miss Y	Judge
Miss A	Miss C	Announcer
Miss B	Miss E	Mr Fairley

(BEFORE YOU BEGIN YOU MIGHT LIKE TO GIVE THE GIRLS NAMES OF
TOWNS AROUND YOUR AREA – MISS Y MIGHT BECOME MISS BRIGHTON,
MISS IPSWICH, MISS GRIMSBY OR SIMILAR.)

*A number of girls are gathered together for a beauty competition.
One or two have been in many competitions and know each
other. Others are there for the first time.*

Announcer's Voice   Ladies and gentlemen the girls will walk
along the side of the pool, turn by the steps and along the
platform to parade in front of the judges. Contestant number
one: Jean is a typist and when she's not showing her shapely
legs off she's reading, playing tennis and listening to music.
Jean is eighteen and measures a delicious 36-24-36.

Miss X *and* **Miss Y** *are waiting to come out.* . . .

Miss X   I'm ever so nervous.
Miss Y   Don't be.
Miss X   No?
Miss Y   This is my fifth contest this year. There's nothing to
worry about.
Miss X   I must say everyone's been really nice. I thought
people were supposed to be catty.
Miss Y   Sometimes they are.
Miss X   Are the competitions ever fixed?
Miss Y   Who knows.
Miss X   Have you ever won?
Miss Y   Second three times.
Miss X   Did you get anything for being second?
Miss Y   Not really.

Pause.

Miss X What makes you keep entering?
Miss Y What made you?
Miss X Just fun I suppose.
Miss Y Vanity, worry, wanting to be called beautiful. Look around . . . ask them all . . . you watch the plastic smiles go on when they walk in front of the judges.
Miss X Yes I see. I suppose this will be the first and only time for me.
Miss Y Not if you're bitten.
Miss X What?
Miss Y Well it's a way into lots of money by modelling if you can win.
Miss X Is it? I only did it for a dare. My friends dared me to enter.
Miss Y You'd better look lively, you're next. Remember smile at the judge in the centre — he's the one who matters today.
Miss X Who is he?
Miss Y A crummy actor.

The **Announcer***'s voice says* . . . 'And next we have Miss X'

Miss Y Good luck. Remember, it's only a cattle market.

Miss X *leaves and* **Miss A** *approaches* . . . .

Miss A She's new isn't she?
Miss Y Yes. Nice girl.
Miss A She doesn't look old enough.
Miss Y Does it matter?
Miss A The rules say you have to be eighteen.

Miss X *is parading in front of the* **Judges**.
The one in the middle speaks to her.

Judge Hello Miss X.
Miss X Hello.
Judge Delightful. What a pretty little thing. It's the eyes I think — sparkling blue. Avril's your name?
Miss X Yes.
Judge What a sweet name! Turn round for us darling. That's splendid Gorgeous . . . we'll see you later in your evening dress. Beautiful . . . Trot off then.

Miss X *walks back as the* **Announcer** *speaks* . . .

31

Announcer   There we are. A lovely girl from the seaside to charm us . . . and indeed doing just that to our head judge . . . enjoying a word of conversation with her there.

Back in the changing room as the girls are changing into evening dress.

Miss A   Zip me up love, will you?

Miss Y   There we are. That's the one you wore in Wales isn't it?

Miss A   Afraid so. It'll have to do though.

Miss Y   (*distracted*) Wow! Look at that . . . (**Miss X** *is putting on a beautiful lace dress*) Where did you get that?

Miss X   I made it.

Miss Y   Made it!

Miss A   It looks like the rest of us are wasting our time. The way you bent the ear of that judge earlier and now this. It's always the same for newcomers. If you've never been seen before you're a novelty.

Miss Y   (*to* **Miss X**) Ignore her. She's getting too old for this game.

Miss A   I'm younger than you.

Miss C   (*calling*) Has anybody got a pin? My zip's gone. I only put it in last night as well.

Miss E   (*going to assist her*) You shouldn't try to cram so much flesh into such a small space.

Miss C   I'm not.

Miss E   Yes you are . . . look at it! If you breathe out you'll burst every seam in the dress.

Miss C   Oh come on and lend me a pin.

Miss E   Hold still then. (*Securing the pin*) I don't want to pin you to the dress.

Miss C   You're an angel.

Miss E   I hope you'll do the same for me.

Miss C   Fear not. (*Looking across at* **Miss X**) What do you think of our new doll?

Miss E   Young, pretty, slim . . . what else is there to say?

Miss C   Likely to walk off with the prize today.

Miss E   So?

Miss C   Didn't you see who was standing by the pool?

Miss E   No.

Miss C   I did.

Miss E   Go on then.

Miss C Guess.

Miss E I can't.

Miss C Tony Small.

Miss E No!

Miss C Yes.

Miss E What's he doing here?

Miss C Everybody he's taken pictures of has ended up in one of the 'glossies'.

Miss E I know. This calls for the effort of efforts. No wonder you're in a mood. Does anybody else know?

Miss C I don't think so. I shouldn't have told you really.

Miss E I'm glad you did. He's here for a reason.

Miss C It's just that neither of us stand a chance with little 'Miss Muffet' around.

Miss E What do you suggest?

Miss C There are ways.

Elsewhere **Miss Y** *and* **Miss B** *are talking.*

Miss B I don't like spoilt schoolgirls hustling us out of our game.

Miss Y She's not.

Miss B She is.

Miss Y You don't know that.

Miss B I'm not going to stand by and let it happen. I'm sure she's below age . . . What does she want out of this lot anyway?

Miss Y Silly question. What do we all want? Be a dear now and shut up. She's coming over.

Miss X Excuse me. Can you tell me where they keep the tissues?

Miss Y There aren't any.

Miss B I'll see you later . . . (*She leaves*)

Miss X I feel as though people are watching me.

Miss Y Course they are. That's what the competition's all about. Here have one of my tissues. . . .

Miss X (*taking one*) Thank you. I feel as though everyone's talking about me . . . talking behind my back.

Miss Y Nonsense. Don't let it worry you. There are other new girls around. They aren't worried. Look . . .

The organiser of the competition, **Mr. Fairley,** *enters. . . .*

Mr. Fairley Excuse me ladies. Is Miss X with us?

Miss X Yes.

Mr. Fairley Ah . . . a word in your ear.

They go outside into the corridor.

Mr. Fairley Look, sorry to disappoint you and all that, but we've had a telephone call from your mum. She wants you home straight away.

Miss X (*surprised and worried*) Oh.

Mr. Fairley Didn't say what for or why dear. She did sound pretty desperate though.

Miss X Thank you.

Mr. Fairley It's a shame dear − I think the judge had a soft spot for you. Perhaps you could try again?

Miss X Didn't she say anything else?

Mr. Fairley No, just . . . "Ask her to come immediately, it's urgent . . . ."

Starting points

1 What does Miss Y mean when she says, 'it's only a cattle market'? Do you agree?

2 What sort of attitude does the judge display? Is it encouraged or discouraged by the people around him?

3 Why does Miss A take a dislike to Miss X and why do you think Miss Y helps Miss X?

4 Do you think there really was a phone call from Miss X's mum? If not − who was it and why?

Discussion points

5 What do you think makes girls want to enter beauty contests? Does the fact that we have beauty contests say anything about the way we live?

6 Is it a good thing to compare and contrast things like bodies, which inevitably fade away? What should we hold as valuable about ourselves?

Written work

7 Who is beautiful to you and why? Write about this person and if you want to disguise the identity you can always call them by a letter or another name.

8 Imagine you are at the competition as a reporter. Write your report saying who won and what your impression of the contest was. Mention that you saw Tony Small there

and include a few comments he made on the contestants.
Mention, also, the disappearance of Miss X.

Action
9 What do the ones who want to be rid of Miss X feel? Is it
jealousy, envy, greed, anger, frustration, distrust, age,
waste, cheated? Improvise the scene where Mr. Fairley
is approached by one or more of the girls who remind him
of the rules of the competition.
10 <u>Face Values</u>. Collect photographs or pictures of people of
a wide age range. Make a note of the changes in expression
and the aging process and what it does to faces. Put the
pictures together and select one pair which interests you
and say what you think that person is like 'underneath' —
either tell the rest of the class or write your ideas for
others to read.
If you have a portable recorder you could ask friends,
teachers, relatives what they consider to be the important
features of a person. You'll probably find that people
value others for what they are and not how they look.
Finally, decide what *you* value most about others.

A Bed Of Nails

Organiser 1   Gordon
Organiser 2   Colin
Organiser 3   Gloria   (teenage friends)
                               Mavis

A small office where three business men are organising details of a proposed venture.

Organiser 1   (*agitated*) Come on now. I'm not putting my money into anything unless I'm sure of a good return.

Organiser 2   I agree. Business is business.

Organiser 3   Well all right. You tell me then. The size of the hall, the attraction for the kids, means we only make thirty per cent profit.

Organiser 1   Three ways makes ten per cent each . . . and I'm no Mr. Ten Per Cent. I want to be sure of doubling my money.

Organiser 3   Impossible.

Organiser 1   There are ways.

Organiser 2   I'm listening.

Organiser 1   Advertise somebody big on the bill.

Organiser 3   Somebody who, big on the bill?

Organiser 1   'Angels'.

Organiser 3   'Angels'! You really are nuts! We don't earn together what they'd charge for a single gig.

Organiser 2   He's right . . .

Organiser 1   Who said anything about paying them?

Organiser 3   They'll do it for nothing?

Organiser 1   They won't even arrive; but every kid in the place will have a ticket saying, 'Appearing live . . . "Angels"' . . . Then in very small type . . . 'circumstances permitting'. We'll announce the 'Angels' can't appear because they've been held up in traffic, or fog, or been taken ill or anything. . .

Organiser 3	We'd never get away with it . . . it's illegal!
Organiser 1	We'd make a mint.
Organiser 2	I like it.
Organiser 1	Question is where?
Organiser 3	I don't like it.
Organiser 1	We need your money, you can't not like it.
Organiser 2	We go ahead and use the Nail Cellar.
Organiser 3	It's too small, what about safety regulations?
Organiser 1	It'll do.
Organiser 3	Impossible. It's not made to hold any more than a few hundred – they'll be like sardines in there. We could go to prison.
Organiser 1	It'll do.
Organiser 2	We're not a charity.
Organiser 1	The eighteenth of next month?
Organiser 2	Could be.
Organiser 3	I still don't like it . . . any of it.

Despite the anxiety shown by **Organiser 3**, *the plans go ahead and the date is fixed.*
The evening of the dance outside the 'Nail Cellar'. Gordon, Colin, Gloria *and* Mavis *are waiting to go in.*

Gordon	I've never seen so many people.
Colin	The queue's a mile long. Look at it. Amazing!
Gloria	It's exciting. Who'd believe it? The 'Angels' coming here. I remember them when they were 'Rock On'. They were good then.
Mavis	They're brilliant now. Their latest album is fantastic.
Colin	They'll never get us all in here.
Mavis	Are we moving yet?
Colin	We don't seem to be. I've never seen so many.
Mavis	Have you got the tickets Gordon?
Gordon	Don't worry. I'm guarding them with my life. Somebody offered me twice the price this afternoon.
Gloria	There are bound to be gate crashers. I know a few people further back who haven't got tickets.

Inside the hall. . . .
The Organisers are waiting.

| Organiser 2 | There are hundreds outside. |
| Organiser 1 | We'll have to play it cool. |

Organiser 3 I knew it — it's a mob not a crowd . . . you'll never control them . . .

Organiser 1 Go and sit in the office if you're going to be hysterical.

Organiser 2 This is our best day's work yet. We can handle it.

Organiser 1 (*shouting*) OK on the door. Let them in.

The door opens and people enter . . . the cellar fills up very quickly and people are soon pressed tightly together. Records are being played prior to the arrival of the group.

Gordon This is painful. You can't move.

Gloria I feel bruised all over.

Mavis I never thought I'd see this place like it . . . it's a wonder it's still standing.

Colin I don't like this very much. There's only one way out — and that happens to be the way in. They must be breaking every regulation that's ever been made.

Gordon Don't worry.

Colin I can't help worrying. This place is likely to collapse any minute. I can't see any fire extinguishers can you?

Gordon I'm not looking.

Colin It won't take much to start a panic; and then what?

Mavis It needs knocking down and rebuilding.

Colin How about standing near the door?

Gordon No way. We'll miss the group.

Gloria We can't pay a fortune and miss it all. We'll be all right.

Gordon It's about time they were here isn't it? What time are they due on?

Mavis No idea, but we seem to have listened to these few records over and over again.

Gloria That's so the group looks better when it comes on.

Gordon (*looking over his shoulder*) Here come the gate crashers. . .

Mavis Oh yes, look at them pushing their way in . . . (*People are pushing and shoving*) . . . Hey . . . watch it! . . . my feet! . . . be careful! . . .

Gloria They're squeezing in everywhere.

Colin Let's get out of here.

Gordon Hold tight a bit.

In the office. . . .

Organiser 3 It's absolutely jam packed out there. They couldn't fall down if they tried. I wash my hands of it.

Organiser 1 Take it easy.

Organiser 2 I think it's time to make an announcement. Say they've been delayed.

Organiser 1 Yeah OK. Start the de-escalation!

Organiser 3 We have big trouble.

Organiser 2 We'd better move fast then. The place is filling up with gate crashers.

Organiser 1 Gate crashers! What gate crashers? We've got bouncers on the doors haven't we?

Organiser 2 It's not enough. Get on the P.A. and make an announcement.

Organiser 3 I wash my hands of it all.

Inside the hall. The P.A. system crackles into life. . . .

Organiser 1 Hi everybody. This is the organiser speaking. We have to ask you to hang on a while longer. The 'Angel's' van has broken down. . . (*Boos from the crowd*) . . . but they're making their way in taxis. Be patient and we'll have them here soon — all being well.

Gordon All being well! What does he mean, all being well!

Mavis There'll be a riot if they don't turn up.

Gloria And I'll be leading it.

Gordon I'll have my money back.

Gloria We haven't seen an organiser — we wouldn't know how to get our money back.

Mavis There's something fishy going on . . . .

A chant begins in the back ground . . . .

We want the 'Angels' . . . . we want the 'Angels' . . . .

Gordon This is where the trouble starts.

Colin Let's get to the door.

Gloria I can't move. I'm tight in all these people.

Gordon Push.

Mavis It's no good. We can't move.

The crowd begin to stamp their feet. . . .

Gloria Good God; the place is rocking!

Colin There's going to be trouble.

The feet get louder. . . .

Mavis   I'm worried Gloria.

Meanwhile, back in the office.

Organiser 3   Listen . . . listen . . . mob hysteria. God knows what you're responsible for.
Organiser 1   *We're* responsible for.
Organiser 2   Get on and announce the cancellation — get it over with.
Organiser 1   Money doesn't come easy to anybody.
Organiser 3   The mob's at our throats. . . .
Organiser 1   Stay calm.
Organiser 2   Let's announce it.

The noise is becoming deafening and there is panic in the air.

Organiser 1   We came into this with our eyes open.
Organiser 3   We planned a disaster!
Organiser 1   Keep cool.
Organiser 3   I can't.
Organiser 2   He's right, it's gone too far — they'll be through these doors any minute.
Organiser 3   I'm going . . . is anybody coming with me?

Starting points
1   When do the young friends begin to realize that they might have been cheated?
2   Why does organiser 3 not pull out of the scheme?
3   What basic attitudes do Organiser 1 and Organiser 2 express?
4   Once in the 'Nail Cellar' why don't the young people stand near to an escape route?

Discussion points
5   Have you ever been in a situation where events have taken over and you have been unable to control the outcome? Why do you think crowds sometimes turn into mobs?
6   The organisers are in it to make money. How important is money to you and how far will you be prepared to stretch the law and your own conscience in order to make or earn it?

Written work

7   Without indulging in a mass of gory detail continue the play and write a suitable conclusion. Show how Organiser 3 behaves and how the gross dishonesty of his associates is resolved.

8   Imagine you are present on the evening and are asked by the police to give a statement. Write exactly what you experienced from the moment you began queueing to get in. You might like to mention where you bought the ticket in the first place.

Action

9   Work out a short play to improvise called 'Small Print' where someone is cheated due to the small print on a contract, a ticket, a competition, an advertisement or something similar.

10 Much of what the Organisers do is against health and safety regulations and the law. Find out as much as you can about these laws and regulations and decide exactly where the organisers were guilty of breaking them. Decide also what sort of penalties should be imposed on offenders.

The Finger

Ricky	Colin
Peter	Tony
Wendy	Headmaster
Anita	Policeman

It is the morning of an important school football match. The players and supporters are arriving.

Ricky Hello Peter.
Peter Hello Ricky. Nervous?
Ricky A bit. I'll be all right once we kick off.
Peter I heard a couple of league scouts were coming up.
Ricky Really?
Peter That's what I heard.

Wendy *and* **Anita** *arrive.*

Ricky Great. Here come our supporters.
Wendy We thought you'd need some cheering today.
Anita Just make sure you beat them. My brother goes to that school and he'll only boast for the next six months if they win.
Ricky They won't.
Peter I can't see anybody beating us. Not the way we've been playing — and with Colin in goal. (*To* **Ricky**) He's had another offer from a second division club you know.
Ricky I know.
Wendy Speak of the devil.
Colin (*joining them*) Morning you lot.
Anita Hello Colin. Are you going to be a famous footballer then?
Colin I hope so. They play at civilised times you know . . . three o'clock in the afternoon.
Anita It does you good getting up early.

Ricky   Before I forget Colin, can I have my comb back?

Colin   What's that?

Ricky   I lent it to you last night after training and you cleared off with it.

Colin   Oh yeah. Sorry, accident I can assure you. It's probably still at the bottom of my bag. I'll give it you when we get changed.

Ricky   All right.

Peter   Are you fit Colin?

Colin   Fit enough.

Tony   (*arriving*) Quick someone, stud spanner. I've got three studs in my boots that I can't get out.

Ricky   I've got pliers; they're better. Come on, let's go into the changing rooms. See you later girls.

Wendy   Don't let them beat you.

Colin   Don't worry. I don't intend to pick the ball out of my net.

Tony   Come on Ricky, let's get my boots sorted out.

The following Monday morning. The **Headmaster** *is addressing the school during morning assembly.*

Head   . . . Dugdale was our scorer and it turned out to be one of his more vital goals as it levelled the score with only two minutes to go. Final score was one each and that means a replay which will take place on Wednesday after school. I needn't remind you that the winners are in the National Final — so any support you can offer would be welcome. And now to a more serious topic and one which sadly consumes me most. Sometime over the weekend the secretary's office was broken into and two hundred pounds stolen. Now I want anyone who has any information at all to come and see me at once. If I hear something before lunchtime I will do everything to help — if I don't then I'll turn the matter over to the police. Needless to say I'm disappointed that this has happened and that suspicion automatically falls on you all assembled here. You have until lunchtime . . . Oh, and I'd like to see Richard Dugdale now please.

The **Head** *goes straight to his study —* **Ricky** *arrives and knocks on his door. . . .*

Head   Enter.

Ricky   (*entering*) You wanted to see me, sir.

Head Ah, Dugdale. Yes. Sit down.

Ricky sits. *The* **Head** *stands and looks out of the window.*

Head Did you see or hear anything on Saturday concerning this theft?

Ricky Not really sir.

Head I've called you in because I want you to make discreet enquiries to see if you can find anything out. As captain of the team you could do that. I know it's not a nice job to snoop on your friends — but the school's involved now and a bad name takes years to live down.

Ricky When did it happen?

Head Saturday morning. There's no sign of damage to outside windows and doors. It's as if the thief had already been in the building, you see . . . so we have to suspect one of our own.

Ricky Or one of theirs?

Head Yes — but the thief knew where to go . . . where to find things.

Ricky I see.

Head Anyway, see what you can find . . . (**Ricky** *stands up to leave*) Oh, and well done on Saturday, it was a great game by all accounts.

Ricky Thank you.

Ricky *leaves the office and meets* **Peter** *in the corridor.*

Peter What did he want?

Ricky Not much.

Peter About the thieving, I suppose?

Ricky Yeah. He just wanted to know if I knew anything about it. I was as surprised as anybody this morning. Have you got any ideas?

Peter I was too busy thinking about the game. Has he asked you to spy round?

Ricky Well yes, but I don't fancy spying on my own mates.

Peter I can't think it was anyone from our side. Maybe Wendy or Anita saw something.

Ricky I doubt it; they stood behind Colin's goal all the game.

Peter I suppose it was some time after, or during half time?

Ricky I don't know where to start. I suppose they'll have to call the police in. Nobody's going to steal and then own up . . . are they?

Peter Can't see how — unless they had a guilty conscience.

44

Ricky Anybody who had a conscience wouldn't steal two hundred pounds.

Wendy (*arriving*) Hello — did he accuse you?

Ricky He's no idea.

Wendy I reckon it was one of their lot. They had a gang of yobs who kept clearing off into the toilets and things.

Ricky I don't suppose you saw anybody by the office did you?

Wendy No. The secretary's doing her nut isn't she.

Peter Why?

Wendy She should have banked the money on Friday. It's a bit bad leaving two hundred pounds in a drawer!

Peter A drawer . . . I thought they'd blown a hole in the safe the way he talked about it in assembly.

Ricky It's still two hundred pounds whichever way you look at it.

Peter I know that, but who could resist it.

Wendy And it was her personal drawer — you know, where she kept letters and private things . . . and they were all over the floor.

Anita arrives. . .

Wendy What happened to your hair?

Anita Very funny. My sister tried to curl it.

Wendy Oh.

Peter Didn't work did it?

Anita No. Who's got a comb and I'll go and do something about it?

Wendy No sorry.

Peter Not me.

Ricky (*feeling in his pocket*) I did have.

Anita Oh never mind, there'll be someone in the loo with one.

She leaves. . .
They split up.
Ricky *walks down the corridor and bumps into* **Colin**.

Ricky Hello Colin.

Colin Hello mate.

Ricky Oh, by the way. . .

Colin Can't stop now. I'm on my way to see Wilkins about my History homework.

Ricky It's just. . .

Colin I'll see you later — OK?

Ricky   About Saturday. . .
Colin   I won't be long. . .

He leaves.
Later that day. No information has come to light and a
policeman has been brought in to speak to the school.

Policeman   We have to treat the thief as a criminal, and everything will be done to trace him or her. Two hundred pounds
was stolen from the office and by the look of things it was
done some time during the morning between 9 o'clock and
twelve thirty. The thief was smart and quick. He or she moved
in, took the money and was out again in an instant. The thief
knew the money was there which means it's probably one of
you people sitting here now.

Pause.

But as with most crimes — it wasn't perfect. The thief left
something and it's a vital clue. . . this!

He holds up **Ricky's** *comb.*

Ricky   (*to himself*) That's mine . . . oh no . . . !

Starting points
1   Why did the headmaster not call the police immediately?
2   What does Ricky feel about having to spy on his friends?
3   How far is the secretary responsible for what happens?
4   What sort of attitude does Colin appear to have?

Discussion
5   Have you ever had to decide whether or not to give
evidence against a friend? What sort of feelings did you
have about it. How do you think Ricky feels about it?
6   Ricky and Peter mention a guilty conscience. What is a
guilty conscience and how does it work?

Written work
7   Continue writing the play as the policeman approaches
Ricky with the words,
'You're the young man who's been leading the investiga-
tion, I hear. Have you come up with any clues?'
8   Imagine the headmaster has to write to the headmaster of

the school involved in the match. Write a tactful letter asking if enquiries could be made regarding the theft.

Action

9 Improvise a scene where the secretary is explaining to the headmaster how she left things on Friday. Consider the anxieties and points of view each will hold.

10 Check the daily papers for a week to see how many 'small' crimes of this nature are reported. Discuss why these crimes are committed and decide on a set of guidelines both for preventing and dealing with offenders. Look as much into the circumstances of the crime and the offender as possible.

Skid Row

Father		**Jeff**	(Maggie's husband)
Mother		**Voice**	Anonymous person
Pauline	(their daughter)		
Maggie	(their daughter)		

Maggie *and* **Jeff** *are living with* **Maggie's** *parents. They are married and are there because their own plans for buying a house have fallen through.*

It is meal time after a hard day for everyone concerned.

Father (*to* **Jeff**) Any luck today young man?

Jeff Afraid not. I've tried every factory in the area now. Still nothing. It's desperate.

Mother Something'll turn up, you'll see. Cup of tea Jeff?

Jeff Yes please.

Maggie We've been everywhere . . . you wouldn't believe it.

Mother I know love. It's just the way things are.

Father (*gruffly*) I've always managed to be in work myself. There's work for those who want it. Maybe you're right Mother, maybe it is just the way things are . . . but I've always managed to be in work.

Maggie (*annoyed by* **Father**) Dad!

Father (*spitefully*) What I do know is, there's a lot of idle so and so's drawing dole money which chaps like me work to pay for. I know that . . .

Mother There's no need for that in front of Jeff.

Jeff (*trying to explain*) I've been everywhere Mr. Trout — been everywhere and offered to do anything. If I go for a labouring job they tell me I'm too well qualified, and if I go for a skilled job they tell me they have no vacancies.

Maggie You can't win Dad — you know that.

Father Maybe . . . any more tea in the pot mother?

Mother (*lifting pot*) No. I can make some more though.

Father No, it's all right. I can do without.
Mother It's no trouble — it'll only take a minute.
Father That's all right. I'll go and read the paper. (*Self righteously*) I've managed without before, I can manage without now.
Jeff (*trying to hold his rage*) Excuse me . . . (*He gets up and storms out*)

Maggie *follows him into the bedroom.* **Jeff** *doesn't speak and begins to pack a suitcase.*

Maggie What are you doing?
Jeff I feel like screaming until the roof comes in. I'm so angry . . . I could . . .
Maggie But what are you doing?
Jeff We're off Maggie.
Maggie Off?
Jeff Going.
Maggie Where?
Jeff Anywhere. Walking the streets, park, bus station — anything. I can't stay here another day.
Maggie That's all right but . . . ?
Jeff I know your mum and dad have been kind and I understand how they're feeling. I might feel the same myself in their position. But what about me? How do I feel?
Maggie I know, and I suppose you're right.
Jeff (*a little surprised*) Are you on my side?
Maggie We're married Jeff. We do things together. It's not your fault you're out of work. You've done everything you could.
Jeff (*trying to sound reasoning*) It's not fair on your mum or dad any more than it is on us. They feel the strain the same as we do.

Maggie's *sister knocks on the door. . .*

Pauline Are you in Maggie?
Maggie What do you want?
Pauline I want a towel from the cupboard.
Maggie I'll get you one. (**Maggie** *reaches one and passes it through the door. . .*) Here . . .
Pauline What's up. Are you hiding something?
Maggie I'm getting changed.
Pauline You're not shy are you?

Jeff   And so am I . . . you can come in if you want.

Pauline   (*embarrassed*) Oh I didn't know you were in Jeff. I'll see you later Maggie.

Jeff   Come on love. Let's get out while we can.

Maggie   I don't expect life to be perfect, Jeff. We'll have bad times as well as good.

Jeff   Everything seemed so easy a couple of months ago. We were married, we put a deposit down on a house and then right out of the blue . . . everything goes wrong . . . when you stop and think about it . . .

Maggie   We'll be all right.

Jeff   I hope so.

Maggie   We'll have to be.

Jeff   We can't afford bed and breakfast . . . or at least we could, but we'll need all our money.

Maggie   What about your sister's?

Jeff   No. It's not fair on her. It'd be the same as here in the end. We can't burden other people with our problem.

Maggie   (*her mind running on*) I don't fancy a station.

Jeff   I know where there are some empty houses . . . just for the night.

Downstairs, some time later in the evening.
Pauline *is watching television with* **Mum** *and* **Dad.**

Mother   I wonder what Jeff and Maggie are doing. They haven't gone out have they?

Pauline   Maggie was getting changed ages ago.

Father   He's probably sulking.

Mother   (*still angry with* **Father**) I don't think so. Jeff's not like that.

Pauline   Something seemed strange to me.

Father   I wouldn't mind that cup of tea now mother.

Mother   All right . . . . (*She gets up*)

Pauline   What did your last servant die of dad?

Father   I want no cheek from you young lady.

Mother   I'll shout up and see if Jeff and Maggie want a cup. (*She goes to the door*) Maggie love . . . Jeff. Cup of tea? Maggie . . .

Outside **Maggie** *and* **Jeff** *are walking along a row of empty houses. It is dark, quiet and very uncomfortable.*

Maggie   Which one Jeff?

50

Jeff Take your pick I suppose. Can't say I know much about how you go about it. Just get in and settle down.
Maggie All right then. Let's pick one we like. (*Mocking sales voice*) The one in the corner has been recently re-wired and extensively modernised. It is a three bedroomed accommodation comprising hall, lounge, dining room, kitchen and bathroom.
Jeff (*joining the joke*) Ideal madam. I'll take it.
Maggie Don't you want to know how much?
Jeff Hang the expense. I can afford the row . . . I'll call it Skid Row.

Silence . . .

Maggie (*dropping the act*) It's pretty depressing.
Jeff Yes.
Maggie I'm just glad we haven't got kids to worry about.
Jeff Sure you don't want to go back?
Maggie Positive.
Jeff I wouldn't mind you know. You could stay with your mum and dad and wait till I found a job and then get a place to live.
Maggie (*being positive*) I like that one on the corner. Come on.

They walk to the house and enter. . . .

Jeff Go easy. It's as black as coal in here.
Maggie I've a torch in my suitcase.

She gets it out and lights the room.

Jeff Not bad. A lot of damp and dirt though. Let's look up stairs.

They walk up the bare staircase and into a bedroom.

Jeff There's a mattress in the corner.
Maggie I couldn't Jeff. Let's try the next one.

They enter the next bedroom.

Jeff It's dirty, but there's a sink. We might be able to organise some water.
Maggie We won't be here for long.
Jeff No. A couple of nights that's all. We can be out during the day looking for work. I'll get something.

51

Silence . . . . Let's sleep then.
Maggie   Yes. Here's your sleeping bag.
Jeff   Thanks.

They lay them out on the floor and climb in.

Jeff   Ready to turn the torch off?
Maggie   Yes. (*She does*)
Jeff   Night love.
Maggie   Sweet dreams.

Pause.

Jeff   You've been really good about this . . . .
Maggie   It's not nice, but there's nothing else for us.
Jeff   It won't be for long. I promise.

They lie in silence.
Eventually they hear footsteps outside and then inside the house.
Someone is creeping about downstairs.

Maggie   (*whispering*) Jeff!
Jeff   I know. I can hear.

The voice calls up into the darkness. . . .

Voice   Anybody up there . . . hello . . . anybody up there?

Starting points
1   Why is the father behaving in such a spiteful way?
2   Why can't Maggie and Jeff go to his sister's?
3   What sort of attitude is the mother displaying . . . why?
4   What impression of married life, and adult life in general, do you think Pauline will be forming now?

Discussion points
5   Is anyone responsible for the situation Maggie and Jeff find themselves in? What can we do or what provision can we make for people so that circumstances like this can be coped with?
6   How far do the responsibilities of parenthood go? Should parents be prepared to house their children as long as there is space available?

Written work

7   Imagine Pauline is asked to write an essay at school called 'The Family'. Write it for her.

8   Imagine you live near the empty houses. Write a letter to the local newspaper stating a point of view about the fact that they are empty and are attracting people who sleep rough.

Action

9   The owner of the voice, whoever it is, persuades Maggie and Jeff to return to the house. Work out the scene as they return and try to sort out the problem with her parents.

10 As a class, invent six other characters who, like Maggie and Jeff, are looking for work and accommodation. Fill in details of their background and identity; the points where things began to go wrong. See if there is anything in common about their misfortunes and try to sort out some firm recommendations and policies which could help people in similar circumstances at the time things go wrong rather than later.

You could present your conclusions in the form of a broadcast which is recorded and includes comment and interviews with the characters involved.

I'll Take It Back

Gale   Gale's Mum and Dad
Trisha   Jean
Shirley

Break time. **Gale, Trisha, Shirley** *and* **Jean** *are in a corner of the school playground.*

Trisha   My mum got me a dress on Saturday. I don't like it . . . I'll never wear it.

Shirley   What's it like?

Trisha   Sort of silky, loose fitting, with a belt.

Shirley   What's wrong with it?

Trisha   I don't know really. I liked it in the shop but when I got home I didn't. It cost a fortune as well.

Jean   You get new things every week.

Trisha   I don't.

Jean   You do. You had new shoes last week.

Trisha   Oh yeah. I forgot. Something else too . . . (*Looking in her bag*) I've got some cassettes for us to play at lunch time.

Shirley   (*interested*) What have you got?

Trisha   Oh loads. I don't know which ones. I just picked a handful up this morning.

Shirley   (*looking at some*) Hey look at these. Terrific. Where did you get them all?

Trisha   My sister buys them mostly. I bought a few.

Gale   Can I see?

Trisha   Help yourself. (*She hands some out*) I don't know what you like.

Gale   I like this. Hey . . . look . . . Jean . . . look!

Jean   Yeah I know.

Trisha   I've got lots here . . . (*She hands out more of them*)

Shirley   Hold on, I'm dropping them . . . (*The cassettes begin to fall and scatter on the ground*)

The bell goes for the end of break.
Trisha wants quickly to retrieve her belongings.

Trisha Typical! Just shovel them into my bag. We've got
Mr Spiller next. I daren't be late for him.
Jean Here. (*The cassettes are gathered up and put into*
Trisha's *bag*)

Later in the day at **Gale's** *house. It is early evening and she and*
her mum and dad are watching television.

Mother You're quiet Gale.
Gale I'm not.
Mother You seem to be.
Gale No.
Dad How's school?
Gale All right, thanks.
Dad Make the most of it . . . they're the best days of your
life.
Mum They weren't for me.
Dad That's what they say though. I wish I'd taken more notice
at school and got qualifications. We'd all be better off now if
I had. That little bit extra in your wage helps you afford the
luxuries.
Mum We don't need luxuries. We might struggle to make ends
meet but we're hard working and honest.
Gale What do you mean mum?
Mum What I say; we have to make do with a little, everyone
knows that . . . it's no disgrace.
Gale No, the other bit.
Mum It's what we are; and I'd hate us to be otherwise. You've
done a good days work Dad, and you know it.
Dad I do but . . . .
Gale (*leaving suddenly*) I'm just going upstairs to my room.

She rushes out.

Mum Gale! (*To* **Father**) That was sudden.
Dad It's as if she remembered something.
Mum Oh well. They say you should let them have their
privacy. I'll give her ten minutes then I'll go and see what the
matter is.

Gale *goes to her room and sits on the bed.*

Gale (*to herself*) . . . Why is it like this? Why is it so difficult? She's got more than me . . . she's got so much more it's not true. She won't miss it. I bet she doesn't even know she's lost it. I hate her . . . I hate her having all that stuff; all those clothes and records and things . . . and she never appreciates it . . . I would if I had lots of things. . . I wish I was working and earning money. I'd buy new clothes and make-up. It's horrible scraping round for things and never looking nice because you can't afford to.

She puts her hand into her pocket and takes out a cassette . . .

I'd work a week for this if I had to. My favourite group: a cassette of my favourite group and she drops it on the floor . . . !

Pause.

All I need now is a recorder to play it on.

She pockets the cassette and pauses by the door before she opens it.

I can't keep it though can I? I knew I wouldn't. I wish I didn't care about things — but I just can't help it. Why can't I not care?
I'll give it back tomorrow. It was a waste of time taking it — I knew I wouldn't have the nerve to keep it. I'll have plenty of time to put it in her bag when she's not looking. Spoilt Trisha. I don't know why the world smiles on her. What about me for a change . . . and my mum and dad?

Gale *opens the door and goes downstairs.*
She enters the lounge . . .

Mum Hello love. Would you like a cup of tea?
Gale Yes please, mum.
Dad No homework tonight?
Gale I've done it.
Dad Done it! You're not getting enough then. You should have homework every night . . . enough to last.
Mum (*shutting* **Father** *up*) Thank you Dad. I think they work hard enough as it is.
Dad It didn't get us anywhere not doing homework.
Mum No but I've already told you we've got the right standards. . . and that's more important than brains.

56

Gale   I'll make the tea mum.
Mum   It's all right love, stay where you are.

She gets up to make it.

The following morning. **Gale** *is entering the school playground.*

Gale   (*to herself*) Where's Trisha? I must find her straight away
and put this back in her bag.
(**Jean** *enters*) Oh hello Jean. Have you seen Trisha?
Jean   No, not yet. I don't want to either . . . she was in a raging
temper yesterday afternoon . . . and you know what her
tempers are like. I'm keeping out of the way.

Shirley *joins them.*

Shirley   Morning girls.
Jean   Hello.
Gale   Hello Shirley. Seen Trisha?
Jean   I'm just telling her about Trisha's mood yesterday and
how she went berserk.
Shirley   She's spoilt, that's her trouble. She gets too much.
Gale   That's true.
Shirley   It's not sour grapes or anything – but I wouldn't like
it. She hasn't any friends you know.
Gale   (*spotting* **Trisha**) Ah look. She's over there.
Jean   Look out, she's coming this way. I'm off before she gets
here. I don't want to be around when she starts again.
Shirley   Ignore her. . . .

Jean *leaves and* **Trisha** *arrives. . . .*

Trisha   Hello. (*Offering sweets*) Want a sweet?
Shirley   (*taking one*) Ta.
Gale   No thanks.
Trisha   I don't like these very much. I don't know why I
bought them.
Shirley   Found your cassette?
Trisha   No, not yet. But I will. I looked all round the playground
and all round the classroom yesterday. I'm going to tell the
headmaster this morning. I'm not having people nicking my
stuff.
Gale   What's the matter?
Trisha   You haven't seen it have you? Somebody pinched one
of my cassettes yesterday.

Gale No.

Trisha Nobody has. My dad's given me a note to take to the headmaster about it. He wants him to get the police up. He says he's sick of all the thieving that goes on.

Shirley Are you sure you didn't just leave it somewhere?

Trisha Positive. It's nowhere to be found. I searched the place yesterday afternoon. It's been stolen and whoever did it's going to have to pay. I'm going to the headmaster now . . .

Gale Can't you wait and see if it turns up?

Trisha No, my dad wants the thief caught.

Starting points

1 Why does Gale take the cassette? Why can't she keep it?
2 Why do you think Trisha has no friends?
3 What sort of attitudes do Gale's parents express?
4 What does Gale feel when she realizes she can't return the cassette without being noticed?

Discussion points

5 How important is the influence of parents on the way we behave? Are sets of values handed down or do they change with each generation? Use Gale and Trisha as starting points.
6 What are the symbols of status among teenagers? How are they acquired and how necessary are they? What sort of emotions do advertisers appeal to?

Written work

7 Write the conversation Trisha and the headmaster might have as she takes her problem to him. They could be joined by the father who has come to complain.
8 Imagine Gale still has the cassette that evening. Write her thoughts as she reflects on the day's happenings.

Action

9 Improvise a scene where Jean and Shirley try to point out to Trisha that she is making herself unpopular by her behaviour and show of possessions. Trisha responds first of all in an aggressive way but then begins to understand.
10 Devise a collective and realistic set of standards and values by which you think a fair society ought to live. Discuss where and why these values might be changed. You could refer to *Animal Farm* by George Orwell and see how the values agreed on by the animals change.

Mother Of Mine

Neil   Pam
Mum   Jane
Roy   Lynn
Bob

Friday evening.
Neil *arrives home later than expected and his* Mum *is waiting.*

Mum Where have you been?
Neil Nowhere.
Mum Nowhere?
Neil Well you know, just messing about at the club.
Mum I thought the club closed at half past ten?
Neil Yeah well. By the time you clear out and that . . . well we just sort of stand around talking.
Mum In the rain?
Neil I won't melt.
Mum I suppose not; but twelve o'clock's too late for you.
Neil Quarter to.
Mum You've got exams to think about.
Neil So?
Mum So. You'll come in when I tell you to. Your dad would have something to say.
Neil Come on mum. I'm not doing anything wrong.
Mum Wait till he gets back.
Neil What about when he gets back?
Mum You take no notice of me. We'll see what your dad can do.
Neil I wish you'd stop nagging me mum. I'm big enough to look after myself now.
Mum You might think you are.
Neil I am. So why do you always have to wait till I come in?
Mum Someone's got to keep control — someone's got to get your supper.

Neil   I can get it myself.

Mum   What do you want . . . a sandwich?

Neil   No thanks.

Mum   Please yourself. I've waited up for nothing have I?

Neil   Oh come on mum. Don't be awkward.

Mum   And who have you been with tonight?

Neil   (*silenced for a moment*) You know who I've been with . . .

Mum   I wouldn't ask if I knew.

Neil   You would.

Mum   Lynn . . . whatsername . . . ?

Neil   You know.

Mum   I don't know anything – I just guess. (*She walks to the door*) . . . Turn the lights off when you go to bed.

The following evening. **Neil, Lynn, Roy, Jane, Bob** *and* **Pam** *are in the club chatting.*

Roy   Anybody fancy seeing that film at Screen Two?

Bob   Seen it.

Roy   Any good?

Bob   Rubbish

Roy   Oh.

Jane   I wouldn't mind – we haven't been to the pictures for weeks.

Pam   Believe me, it's not worth it. It costs the earth to get in as it is. You expect more for your money.

Lynn   I'd rather go and see the sea.

Bob   Pardon?

Lynn   Well I would.

Roy   It's a long way to go for a night!

Lynn   I mean for the day. You could have a day trip to the coast for what it costs to see a film.

Jane   Good idea.

Bob   Yeah. Good idea. I wouldn't mind. We could have a laugh.

Pam   Yeah, why don't we? We could go early and come back late.

Bob   I'll find out train times. Who fancies going?

Jane   We do, don't we Roy?

Roy   OK.

Pam   Neil?

Lynn   Come on Neil, let's go.

Neil   Why not. It sounds like a great idea. I think there's a train back about midnight . . . we used it once when we'd been on holiday.

Bob That's it then . . . it's decided, we'll have a day out.

Later that evening. Neil *is walking* Lynn *home.*

Lynn You were quiet tonight.
Neil Was I?
Lynn You know you were.
Neil I don't. I'm no different than usual.
Lynn Come on Neil — you can't fool me.
Neil It's nothing.
Lynn Don't you fancy a day out at the seaside?
Neil I do yeah.
Lynn I thought it would be a good excuse for us to be together for a day. We don't have to stay with the others all the time.
Neil I know. It's a great idea — I really like the idea of being with you.
Lynn Good. I'll make us some sandwiches and that — just like an old married couple. Let's go soon Neil.
Neil All right.
Lynn (*persuading*) Next weekend?
Neil (*hesitating*) Ah . . . ?
Lynn Come on Neil . . . next weekend.
Neil OK.

Thursday tea time. Neil *is watching TV. His* Mum *is clearing the table.*

Mum I had a letter from your dad this morning.
Neil Oh yeah?
Mum He's having to stay over another week.
Neil Oh?
Mum That means he'll miss another weekend.
Neil Yeah.
Mum I was hoping you might help me decorate the bathroom now that your dad won't be back.
Neil Me?
Mum Why not? You're big enough. That's what you keep telling me anyway.
Neil When?
Mum Weekend.
Neil Which bit of the weekend?
Mum Which bit! Every bit. It's not a five minute job.

Neil I don't think I can.

Mum Oh and why not?

Neil Ah . . . I . . . I'm sure there's something I'm supposed to do.

Mum It can't be very important if you can't remember. That bathroom's a disgrace.

Neil Not this weekend mum.

Mum I've set my mind on it Neil. I bought the paint and wallpaper this morning. I'll show it to you. (*She leaves to get it and returns*) You have to be prepared to help out about the house now you're old enough. (*Holding the paper out*) . . . What do you think . . . do you like the colour?

Saturday morning. The railway station. The group of friends have bought tickets and are waiting for the arrival of **Neil**.

Bob What time is it?

Roy Ten to.

Bob He's pushing it a bit.

Roy Yeah, if he doesn't get here soon I don't know what we're going to do.

Bob Go I suppose.

Roy Yeah, but what about Lynn?

Lynn, **Pam** *and* **Jane** *are standing by the ticket office.*

Jane Don't worry. Something must have stopped him.

Pam There's another train at eleven.

Jane We could get that. You did tell him the time didn't you . . . ?

Lynn (*upset*) 'Course I did. He knows . . . I knew he wouldn't come.

Pam He'll be here Lynn.

Back with **Bob** *and* **Roy** . . . .

Bob You know what?

Roy What?

Bob I bet his old lady's at the bottom of this.

Starting points

1 Why is Neil's mum waiting up for him on the Friday evening?

2 Why do you think Neil is reluctant to agree to the day trip?

3   What is Neil's mum's attitude towards his girlfriend? Why
    do you think she has this attitude?
4   Where do you think the father is?

Discussion points
5   Why should a mother be like this about her child? Is it
    acceptable? What do you think she stands to gain by it?
6   What sort of 'return' should parents expect? How much
    help in the home and how much time and attention should
    a son or daughter give?

Written work
7   Write a scene where parents and children are clashing over
    some problem or other. It could be that the parents want
    a family holiday together and the son and daughter want
    to go with their own friends.
8   Imagine the father telephones on the Saturday evening.
    Write the conversation he has with Neil's mother.

Action
9   Neil has to let down either his mother or Lynn. Depending
    on the ending you have chosen, act out the scene where
    the injured party accuses Neil of being ungrateful or
    cowardly. It could begin, 'You could have told me Neil,
    is it too much to ask . . . ?'
10 Can you think of any authors who have written about this
    problem of parents hanging on to their children? Find
    some of their work and after reading passages discuss the
    various points of view expressed. Interview your friends in
    school to find out when they think parents should
    encourage their children to be responsible for their own
    actions. Ask them also, whether they think too much or
    too little concern is damaging.

I Can't Stop Now

Nurse	Sister
Mr Long	Mother
Mrs Long	Foreman
Eric	Boss

The District **Nurse** *is visiting* **Mr.** *and* **Mrs. Long.** *They are in their seventies and* **Mr. Long** *has recently been ill.*

Nurse   Take these tablets after meals Mr. Long and they will help you stop feeling dizzy.

Mr Long   Thank you.

Nurse   (*turning to* **Mrs. Long**) Have you anyone to help you with housework and things?

Mrs Long   Oh yes. I've got neighbours, nurse. They all know me.

Nurse   Are you sure now?

Mrs Long   We'll be all right nurse. What's wrong with him nurse? He keeps feeling sick.

Nurse   He's has a bad dose of the 'flu Mrs. Long. He's recovering but it's not easy for you to be running round nursing a sick man. You must take care of yourself you know. Eat properly, won't you.

Mrs Long   Oh, I will nurse, I will.

Nurse   Good. Well I'll be off. I'll be back tomorrow morning about ten o'clock.

Mrs Long   All right.

Nurse   OK then. Don't hesitate to ring me or the doctor if you need us . . . you have the number haven't you?

Mrs Long   Yes . . . yes . . . It's in my handbag.

Nurse   Cheerio then.

She leaves.

Mr Long   Has she gone?

Mrs Long   Yes.

Mr Long   I don't feel well.

Mrs Long   I know you don't, that's why you're ill.

Mr Long   Can I have a cup of tea?

Mrs Long   Yes. I'll make you one.

Mr Long   I wish I felt better. I don't like being like this all the time. I wish I was young again.

Mrs Long   If wishes were horses beggars would ride.

Mr Long   I know, but, it's cruel isn't it? Helpless like this and needing other people to look after us.

Eric, a young man who is a neighbour of the Long's, enters work half an hour late. The **Foreman** *approaches him.*

Foreman   (*displaying his watch*) What time is it?

Eric   (*breathless*) Half past.

Foreman   What does that make you?

Eric   Late.

Foreman   Right first time.

Eric   So?

Foreman   So!

Eric   What's a few minutes. I work hard, don't I?

Foreman   (*angry*) You're half an hour late and it's the second time this week. Once last week, three times the week before.

Eric   I explained about that.

Foreman   Oh did you . . . did you? Well maybe you'd better explain to the boss, because I'm fed up of taking your back-chat.

Eric   (*half pleading*) Come on . . .

Foreman   No. You come with me . . . (*He leads the way*)

Eric follows protesting.
They reach the boss's office, knock on the door and enter.

Boss   What's the problem?

Foreman   I've had enough from this chap, boss. You'd better see what you can do with him.

Boss   Oh . . .

Foreman   He's late, again.

Eric   He's making something out of nothing gaffer; honest he is.

Boss   (*he takes a file out of his desk*) Now then, Eric, I'm not in the habit of being heavy handed, you know that, but I'm not having you upsetting the apple cart. Your work's good but your time-keeping's lousy. It looks to me like you've been making a habit of this late starting.

65

Eric I've explained about that . . . I told the foreman.

Boss Well let me do some explaining. If you are late again this week, next week or the week after you can consider yourself unemployed because I'm not having this sort of thing going on.

Eric But . . .

Boss I hope it's clear . . . come late and you're sacked — all right?

Eric *turns and walks out of the office.*

Foreman Thanks Mr. Goodwin.

Boss No problem George. If he's late let me know — we can fill his job ten times over.

Later at home. **Eric** *is having tea with his* **Mother** *and* **Sister**.

Mother What's the matter, the cat got your tongue? (*No reply*) . . . Eric . . .

Eric What?

Mother What's the matter?

Sister Can I stay home from school tomorrow mum?

Mother Certainly not, why?

Sister We've got maths.

Mother Ridiculous!

Sister I'll be glad when I can leave.

Mother That's a long time away for you, so learn what you can while you can.

Sister I hate it.

Eric (*finishing*) Any pudding?

Mother Manners! And what is the matter with you?

Eric Nothing.

Mother There must be something. I've never known you so quiet.

Eric I got in trouble for being late this morning.

Sister Serves you right.

Eric You can be quiet.

Mother What did they say?

Eric The boss said if I'm late again I'll get sacked.

Mother Eric!

Eric He's just being awkward.

Mother Right. You set that alarm clock half an hour earlier tomorrow morning and make sure you get there on time. Do you understand?

Eric Yeah.

Mother You've got away with far too much recently.

The following morning. Eric is asleep. The alarm clock is ticking loudly. It rings and is stopped. Eric groans a little but slumps down into the bed. The clock continues ticking and Eric sleeps on.

At the same time in the Long's house...

Mr Long I feel dizzy; like I'm going to black out.

Mrs Long Lie still then, I'll get your medicine.

Mr Long That's no good, I know it's not.

Mrs Long Don't make a fuss now. The nurse said you'd be worse at night.

Mr Long What time is it?

Mrs Long Quarter past seven.

Mr Long I think you'd better ...

He loses consciousness...

Mrs Long Dear Lord! Wake up ... what's wrong? Oh what should I do? ... Get a neighbour, call for an ambulance ... get the nurse.

Mr Long comes round...

Mr Long What time is it? Oh my head and my chest aches ... I'm thirsty ... can you get the nurse?

Mrs Long Are you all right?

Mr Long No, I'm worried. I can't see you very well.

Mrs Long You just went unconscious.

Mr Long I will do in a minute if you don't get the doctor. I feel ill.

Mrs Long I'll go and get the doctor or the nurse. Which is best? Now if I can find my bag I can find the number.

Mr Long Will you get me a drink of water. I feel dry. I've never felt so dry. Will you get me a drink?

Mrs Long I will. I'll just go and get the nurse. Are you all right whilst I do that?

Mr Long Have you got money?

Mrs Long Yes.

Mr Long What are you going to do, you can't get to the telephone.

Mrs Long I'll ask someone, there's bound to be someone passing. Don't worry.

She leaves the house and enters the street. It is empty so she waits.

Back at home. **Eric** *wakes with a start and realizes he has overslept again. He hastily dresses and washes muttering to himself all the time. He hasn't time for breakfast and he bangs on his mother's bedroom door as he leaves shouting that it's time to get up. He picks up his coat and rushes out into the street. He runs towards the bus stop and almost falls over* **Mrs. Long.**

Mrs Long Hello Eric love. Can you help me love? I've been waiting a few minutes and I don't like to leave him. Here's the number and some coppers, can you ask them to come right away . . . he passed out just now and . . .

Eric What's wrong?

Mrs Long I want you to go to the telephone for me.

Eric I'm sorry, Mrs. Long. I can't stop now . . . .

Starting points

1   Why can't Eric stop? Whose fault is it that he can't?
2   Should Mr. Long have been taken into hospital care?
3   Should Eric's mum make more of an effort to be up herself so that she might encourage him to be on time?
4   What sort of attitude does Eric's sister have?

Discussion points

5   Whose responsibility should it be to watch over and help old people? Is it a job for the community, for the country, for the family or for the hospitals?
6   If Eric had stopped to help and then lost his job because of it what sort of attitude do you think he would have developed? Would he have blamed just the one incident with Mrs Long for his downfall or his own performance over recent weeks?

Written work

7   Write the conversation between Mr and Mrs Long as she returns to say she can't get anyone to telephone.
8   Imagine the boss is in the local pub the evening of the warning. He is talking about young people and quoting Eric as an example of what's wrong with them. Write an account of what happens as various people join in the conversation and offer different views.

Action

9 It is often difficult to apologise. Imagine you are in Eric's position: work out a scene where you go back to Mrs Long's house after work and try to explain why you couldn't stop.

10 Eric might be able to claim unfair dismissal if he was sacked for helping Mrs Long. Find out as much as you can about Industrial Law and apply it to this case. You could turn the classroom into a room where a hearing was to take place. The characters could be questioned and examined and you could expand the cast list to include many new people. Decide on a verdict and give recommendations on how these sort of situations can be avoided in future.

What Price You?

Margaret	Shop Owner
Tracy	Manageress
Sally	Doorman

Margaret and Tracy are working in 'Young Fashions' a clothes boutique as part-time assistants. It is Saturday morning and they overhear part of a conversation between the Owner of the shop and the Manageress.

Owner   Look at these stock-lists and compare them to sales.

Manageress   Yes I see.

Owner   We've done most things to stop shop lifting but it does seem unacceptably high. We're down twenty to thirty pounds each week.

Manageress   We've prosecuted everyone we've caught. As you see the expensive coats are chained to the rail, but these smaller items just have to be available. People have to be able to pick them up and handle them — it's bad for selling if they can't.

Owner   That may be, but the business can't go on as it is; profit margins are slender enough. . . .

Sandra   He's at it again.

Tracy   It won't stop him running his sports car though, will it?

Sandra   Suppose not. I wouldn't like shop work full time, would you?

Tracy   I wouldn't mind — there are perks. . . .

A customer, Margaret, enters. She is a friend of Tracy's.

Sandra   I'll go.

Tracy   No it's all right I know her.

Sandra   We'll both go.

Tracy   OK.

They approach Margaret.

Tracy Hello.

Margaret Hello Tracy.

Sandra Can we help you?

Margaret I'm looking for a blouse, preferably pink.

Sandra Yes. Here are your sizes. (*Indicating*) This rail and this one. . . .

Margaret Thank you. (*She begins to look*)

Tracy Anything special you were looking for, Margaret?

Margaret A satiny sort of material.

Tracy How about this one?

Margaret Something like that.

Sandra That'll suit you.

Margaret Trouble is, I don't like the rose on the collar.

Sandra You could always take it off.

Margaret It might spoil it if I did that.

Tracy What about something else?

Margaret Not really. This was the one I wanted — but for the rose.

Sandra I'm sure you could take the rose off — it's only stitched on.

Margaret I think I'll leave it. You haven't anything else in pink and that's the colour I need. Thanks anyway . . . thanks, Tracy.

Tracy OK Margaret. I'll see you tonight.

Margaret See you.

She leaves.

Tracy I'm ready for a sit down. The thing about shop work is it murders your legs.

Sandra What are you doing tonight?

Tracy Disco. Usual. You?

Sandra Don't know.

Tracy Don't know! Has Michael not told you yet?

Sandra (*sheepishly*) I'm not going out with him any more.

Tracy What!

Sandra Yes.

Tracy Why? I thought you two were ready to settle down and buy a house.

Sandra I don't know really. We just sort of stopped.

Tracy Who did the stopping?

Sandra Both of us.

Tracy Both?

Sandra I suppose it was more him than me.

Tracy Well, well, well . . . So you're at a loose end?

Sandra Sort of. I wondered if . . . .

Tracy Come with us if you like. There's always a crowd of us go to the disco.

Sandra Can I?

Tracy I suppose so.

Sandra Thanks ever so much.

Tracy That's all right. You take things as you find them though.

Sandra I want to enjoy myself a bit before I start going steady again.

Tracy I don't rate going steady. It's like dry rot. . . (*Pause*) . . . 8 o'clock then . . .

Sandra Sorry?

Tracy The disco, we'll meet inside.

Sandra Oh yeah thanks. . . thanks a lot.

Later that evening in the disco.
Tracy *and* Margaret *are talking.*

Margaret Thanks for getting the blouse.

Tracy That's all right.

Pause.

Margaret I unpicked the rose in five minutes.

Tracy Yes. What time is it?

Margaret Half eight.

Tracy (*surprised*) Is it?

Margaret Why? Are you expecting someone?

Tracy Sort of.

Margaret What do you mean sort of?

Tracy Sandra from the shop.

Margaret The girl who was with you this morning?

Tracy Yes.

A long pause. . .

Margaret Is she all right?

Tracy A bit old fashioned.

Margaret Why did you invite her?

Tracy Why not? Her boyfriend's finished with her. She had nobody to go out with. You know what it's like when you've been tied to the whim of a boyfriend for months you feel like a castaway. Anyway she asked, at least she wanted to ask — I could tell.

Margaret It's asking for trouble isn't it?

Tracy I couldn't do anything else. She won't say anything. . .
Anyway, it doesn't look like she's coming so we'll not have
to worry about it will we?

Margaret I wouldn't have worn this blouse if I'd known.

Tracy Don't worry.

Sandra *is at the door. She is being prevented from entering
by a* **Doorman.**

Doorman You can't come in unless you're signed in by a
member.

Sandra I want to join.

Doorman You can't without a member.

Sandra I was supposed to be meeting my friend, but my
dad's car wouldn't start and I was late.

Doorman I can't help that love. We have rules and that's it.

Sandra Well can I see if my friend's inside then? She can come
out and sign.

Doorman (*exasperated*) Why does everything have to be so
difficult? We have a rule, so why . . .? Oh I give up — go on
but be quick. If you're not back in five minutes I'll send in
the bouncers.

Sandra Thank you.

Sandra *enters hurriedly searching for* **Tracy.** *She spots her
sitting with* **Margaret.** *She goes over.*

Sandra Tracy.

Tracy Sandra! We'd given you up for lost. You remember
Margaret — you met her in the shop this morning.

Sandra Oh yes . . . (*She recognises the blouse*) You got it
after all . . . ?

Margaret Yes.

Sandra I said it would be all right without the rose.

Margaret You did. Excuse me. (*She leaves*)

Tracy Well?

Sandra Can you come and sign me in?

Tracy 'Course . . . (*Halting*) You do recognise that blouse?

Sandra Yes.

Tracy And you put two and two together?

Sandra Well — yes. You took it.

A pause as they both reflect and accept the situation . . .

Tracy Fair enough, let's sign you in.

Starting points

1 How do you reconcile Tracy's thieving with the kindness and understanding she shows towards Sandra when Sandra is looking for an invitation?
2 What is Margaret's reaction when she hears Sandra is coming?
3 Why does Sandra overlook the fact that Tracy is stealing? How much is she involved by it?
4 What would be your reaction if you were Sandra?

Discussion points

5 What lengths will we go to to make sure we have friendship or companionship?
6 You could say it was a coincidence that events happened the way they did. What do you think? Is coincidence of this nature inevitable or is it purely chance?

Written work

7 Margaret is obviously embarassed by the spread of knowledge to Sandra. Imagine they meet later at the disco and talk. . . . Sandra might begin, 'I won't say anything you know. . . '
8 It has been said that everybody has a price. Show whether you understand this to be true or not by writing your own story. You might like to call it, 'The Bribe'.

Action

9 Improvise the scene the following Saturday when the owner and manageress suspect their staff and interview Sandra and Tracy separately.
10 Motives — people's reasons for doing things are often very complicated and strong.
   Write down and discuss the motives of every character in the play. How do motives originate and how can we channel them to be useful?
   Can you think of famous people who have been highly motivated? What were their motives and where did they lead them?

When I'm 64

Phil
Sandra (his girlfriend)
Tony
June (Phil's friends)

Eddie
Laura
Foreman

Phil *is reluctantly starting his working life and has just been introduced to* **Eddie** *who will supervise him for the first two weeks.*

Eddie (*in a friendly way*) So you're keen to work in engineering are you?

Phil Yes and no.

Eddie (*surprised*) Yes and no! What kind of an answer's that? (*indicating his lathe*) It's a magnificent piece of machinery this. It can provide work exact to parts of a thousand and make 'em shine like marble. You'll be a long time mastering this animal.

Phil How long did it take you?

Eddie All my life son, apart from the war, and I'm sixty-four years old.

Phil That's a long time.

Eddie You're right it is.

Phil Is that what I've got to look forward to?

Eddie You're lucky to have a job. There's hundreds unemployed.

Phil I know.

Eddie It's bread and butter — it's your livelihood son.

Phil OK.

Pause. . . .

Eddie Well let's get down to it then. Get your overalls on and then we can go round the machine and learn about its parts and capabilities.

That evening **Phil** *talks to his friends* **Sandra, Tony** *and* **June** *in a coffee bar.*

Tony   What's it like to be one of the nation's wage earners?
Phil   Horrible if today's anything to go by.
Tony   First day's always the worst. It's bound to be.
Phil   I suppose so. It's just the thought of being tied to a machine for the next hundred years that worries me.
Tony   It's a job.
Phil   I know, and I know it's my own fault that I haven't got anything different. I'm lazy, I always have been. I'll stick it, but I can't promise I'll like it.
Sandra   You want to be working in an office all day. I sometimes think I'm going to scream. I even put cotton wool in my ears. . . .
June   I like my job. Hairdressing's great. It's different all the time. I'm going to have my own shop one day.
Tony   I suppose this is what they mean when they say 'You wait' and 'Your turn will come. . . ' and things like that. . . .
Phil   Who?
Tony   Parents and teachers.
Sandra   It'll be all right when we're married Phil. I'll be able to stay at home and have babies.
Phil   Married! Babies! One heart attack at a time thank you. I've to be up at seven o'clock tomorrow morning, and the prospect doesn't delight me.
Tony   (*laughing*) That's known as making a man out of you.
Phil   Man! . . . Zombie more like.

Meanwhile **Eddie** *is at home talking to his wife.*

Eddie   What's wrong with young people today?
Laura   Pardon.
Eddie   I mean they've never had it so good. Washing machines, fridges, National Health, schools . . . nobody goes hungry. Not one man, woman or child need go hungry in this country, and they're still not satisfied.
Laura   What makes you say that?
Eddie   Oh it's the attitude. I've a young lad started with me today.
Laura   What's wrong with him?
Eddie   There's nothing wrong with him.
Laura   What then?

76

Eddie Well I don't know — he's not interested you see: doesn't care: doesn't want to know: thinks it's all a waste of time.

Laura Eddie. . .

Eddie They don't seem to take a pride in things any more. The quickest, easiest way to the most comfort and pleasure, that's their idea.

Laura You're talking like an old man.

Eddie Nonsense. I'm observing that's all. Comparing it with my day.

Laura That's a mistake.

Eddie Things are certainly different.

Laura It's not easy you know.

Eddie What isn't?

Laura Being young.

Eddie Come on Laura.

Laura Oh no it isn't — you might think it is but it isn't. Are you sure you wouldn't like some supper . . . ?

Two weeks later.

At work. **Phil**'s *attitude is quite different now and he is beginning to enjoy his work.*

Phil Morning Eddie.

Eddie Hello Phil. OK?

Phil Yes thanks.

Eddie I reckon you're ready for you own machine. What do you think?

Phil Sure Eddie. I can't wait.

Eddie I've done a good job on you, you know.

Phil You'll be wanting thanks next.

Eddie Apart from your manners, you're not a bad lad now.

Phil I enjoy it Eddie. I never thought I would — but I like making things. It's good.

Eddie Making things! You're turning lumps of raw steel into intricate components.

Phil That's what's good — making them. I like being with fellas instead of kids and teachers.

Eddie Is that right?

Phil Yeah well. It's real this . . . not like school.

They are interrupted by the **Foreman.**

Foreman Morning you two.

Eddie Good morning.

Foreman Pop up and see the boss sometime this morning, Eddie, will you.

Eddie The boss!

Foreman The man himself.

Eddie What does he want?

Foreman How should I know? I only carry his messages.

He leaves. . .

Eddie I wonder what he wants?

Phil You'd better go and find out.

Eddie Do you think so?

Phil Certainly.

Eddie Right then; this is the first time you know.

Phil Go on.

Eddie *leaves.*
Phil *stands by the machine.*
The **Foreman** *returns.*

Foreman What's the matter with you — turned to stone?

Phil No, I'm just waiting for Eddie — he's gone to see the boss.

Foreman Well get on with it. You don't need Eddie do you? You can operate this machine can't you?

Phil Yes.

Foreman Get cracking then . . . you've wages to earn.

Phil Right . . . (*He starts*) . . .

Later that evening **Eddie** *and his wife,* Laura, *are at home having supper.*

Laura Quiet.

Eddie What?

Laura I said you're quiet.

Eddie Am I?

Laura What's wrong?

Eddie Nothing's wrong.

Laura (*hurt*) Sorry. . .

Eddie I can sit here quietly without being chewed at all the time can't I?

Laura Yes.

Eddie (*realising he's being hurtful*) I'm sorry.

Laura You haven't said a word since you walked in. How am I supposed to know what's wrong, whether to speak or not.

78

I hate that, you know I do.

Eddie I know, love.

Laura Something's going on, isn't it? I can tell when you're like that — you ignore me and think I'm stupid.

Eddie It's hard suddenly to realize that it's over.

Laura What do you mean, over?

Eddie That you've had your life and it's somebody else's turn.

Laura What are you talking about?

Eddie They've asked me to take redundancy today.

Laura Redundancy?

Eddie They were nice; offered me a lump sum and what not.

Laura Oh?

Eddie They want to make way for young Phil. They need new blood and since he's turned out all right . . . well they've asked me.

Laura I see.

Eddie It's the waste that breaks your heart. All those years experience and suddenly nobody wants it.

Laura What will you do?

Eddie Well . . .

Laura Will you take it?

Eddie I don't know that I can get used to the idea of being an old man. Despite appearances, I'm as young as a kitten inside.

Starting points

1 What is Eddie's reaction to the offer of redundancy — why does it come as such a shock?

2 What were some of Phil's friends attitudes towards work?

3 Why do you think Phil felt so unhappy about starting work?

4 Why do you think his attitude changed so much after two weeks?

Discussion points

5 Do you think people generally find the satisfaction that Eddie finds and Phil is beginning to find in their work?

6 What do you expect from work? What should it give in return for your time and effort and skill? What part does it play in a person's life?

Written work

7   Eddie and his wife have a strong relationship. Continue
     writing the conversation to discover how they talk the
     problem through.

8   Imagine you are a member of Parliament and have to make
     a speech to a large number of employers. Write the speech
     which argues the case for making better use of people like
     Eddie who still has a lot to offer industry and society.
     Suggest that we make more of our old people and stop
     taking useful and enjoyable work away from them.

Action

9   It is the year 2000 and Phil has just been asked by his boss
     to accept redundancy pay. Act out a scene where Phil
     goes home to his wife Sandra and during the evening the
     news comes out. Will the scene be anything like the situa-
     tion Eddie and Laura were in during the play?

10   Ask your parents and older relations what their attitudes
     towards work are and whether or not they get job
     satisfaction. Find out how they view the prospect of
     retirement and ask what their impressions of young people
     are.
     Collect these interviews on a tape, and by adding a
     commentary, make a radio programme.